The Prince & the Pauper

A long time ago in the old city of London a baby named Tom Canty was born to a family of paupers in the poor neighborhood of Offal Court. Meanwhile in Westminster, a place not very far away at all, but might as well have been a world away, another boy named Edward was born to the royal family.

2

As the years went by, Tom Canty was sent out by his father to beg for food and money every day. Tom's father was very mean and selfish, and if Tom came home empty-handed, he would beat him and send him to bed hungry.

One day, desperate to return home with something, Tom tried begging in a different neighborhood. He wandered around the fancy streets until before he knew it, he had arrived at the royal palace.

Although he knew it was forbidden to stop at the palace's wrought iron gates, his curiosity got the best of him, and he couldn't help but try to get a peek inside. And there he saw the little boy who had been born on the same day as him: Prince Edward.

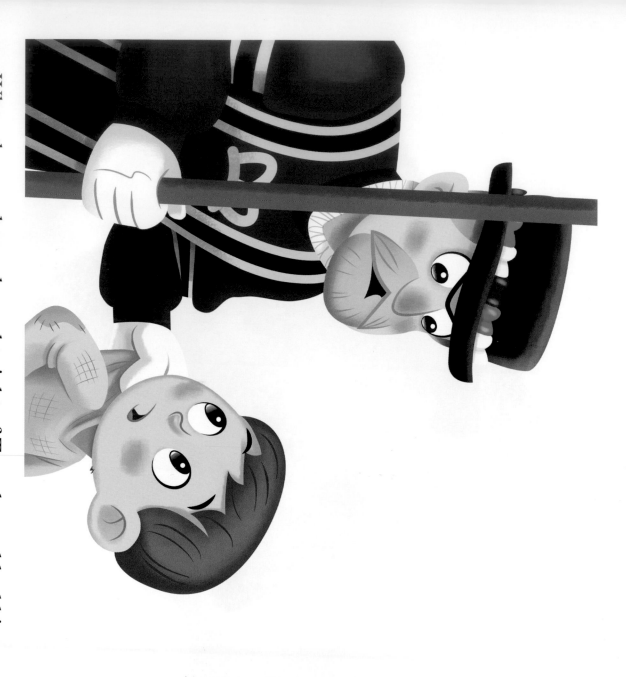

When the royal guard caught sight of Tom, he grabbed him roughly by the collar, and shouted, "Get out of here! Go back to your own neighborhood! Paupers are not welcome here!"

6

Prince Edward, who was nearby on the other side of the gates, heard everything. He felt bad for Tom. "Open the gates!" he demanded. "Guard, you should not have handled this poor boy so roughly." Then he took Tom into the palace with him.

The prince guessed that Tom was hungry, so he had a delicious meal prepared for his new friend, and then took him on a tour of the castle. Edward told Tom all about his life as a prince, and Tom thought that it all sounded fantastic. Since Tom was little he had always dreamed of being a prince!

When the prince asked Tom about his life, Tom explained that he spent lots of time on the streets of Offal Court, and that when he wasn't busy talking to strangers and begging, he played with his friends. The prince, who was tired of being cooped up alone in the castle, thought this sounded like tremendous fun.

So, the two boys, who happened to look very much alike, decided to trade clothes for the day just to see what it would feel like to be the other person.

Once Prince Edward was dressed as a pauper, he thought it would be fun to go for a walk around the palace grounds. But when he arrived at the gate, he was in for a surprise.

The guard, who was still sore about having been scolded earlier for trying to get rid of Tom, mistook the prince for the pauper. When he saw that the pauper was alone, he whacked him with the end of his royal polearm, and kicked him off the grounds.

Edward pleaded, "Guard, do you not recognize me? It is I, Prince Edward, dressed in the pauper's clothes!" But the guard wouldn't listen. He closed the gates, and there was no way to get back inside.

So Edward wandered through the streets until he reached Offal Court. He told everyone in Tom's neighborhood that he was really the prince, but nobody believed him. They just thought that it was Tom, and that he had gone completely mad.

Suddenly a man grabbed Edward and carried him off. It was Tom's father, and he was angry that the boy he thought to be his son had not collected a single coin or crumb of food. He took him home to their shabby shack.

Meanwhile back at the castle, Tom was enjoying life as a prince. He had been hungry for so long that when he sat at the royal table, he gobbled up all the food that was brought to him, plate after plate.

No one at the castle questioned who he was since he looked exactly like the prince. When he behaved in a strange or un-royal manner, they all just thought that he was joking.

14

Although the silk clothes felt good against his skin, and the food filled his belly, Tom was soon overwhelmed by all the royal duties he had to perform. In fact, he couldn't keep up, and he began to long for the return of the real prince.

When he tried to explain that he was not the prince, no one paid any attention, preferring to believe that the prince was either a great prankster or worse, slowly going insane.

Then one day, a messenger arrived with the news that King Henry, Prince Edward's father, had died. This meant that Prince Edward was now the king, which meant that everyone thought Tom was the king! What was he going to do?

16

Meanwhile, back in Offal Court, the real prince was miserable and desperate. Tom's father was treating him like a slave. Edward worked and begged all day, and if he was lucky, he would be given some stale bread to eat before bed.

I must get out of here! thought Edward. So, the first chance he got, he ran off into the crowded streets of Offal Court, where he heard that his father had died, and that the prince had become the king of England.

Edward pleaded with the crowd. He was now the true king of England, and needed to get back to the castle. But everyone mocked him… everyone except a man named Miles Hendon.

Miles Hendon took pity on the boy. He wasn't sure if he was telling the truth, but the crowd was becoming angry, and he feared for the boy's safety, so he agreed to take him to the palace.

When they arrived, the guard refused to let them in. "There is no way that this boy before me can be the prince. It's Coronation Day and the real prince is inside waiting to officially become the king of England," he said.

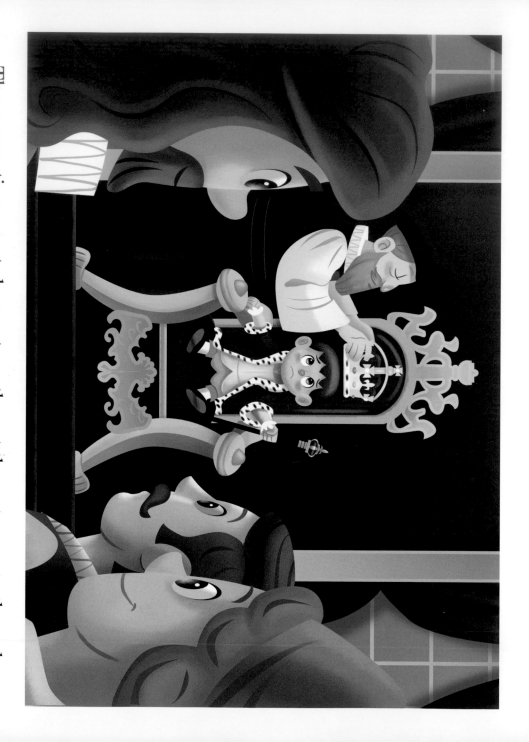

The coronation guests began to gather at the entrance to the palace, and when the gates were finally opened, Edward and Miles snuck past the guard with all the guests.

When they reached the grand hall, Edward saw Tom sitting miserably on the throne. He was loudly protesting that he was not the prince, and that he was instead a poor boy from Offal Court.

Then, Tom heard Edward's voice: "The boy speaks the truth!" he shouted, pointing. "He is not the prince. He is Tom Canty from Offal Court, and I am Prince Edward, the son of King Henry!"

Tom was so relieved! He confirmed that the boy who had just stepped forward was telling the truth! "That is the real Prince Edward!" he said, smiling. "He is the one that should be up here on this throne, and not I!"

But it was not easy to switch back to their rightful roles. The royal court needed proof. In order to determine the true identities of the boys, they wanted to know the location of the Great Seal of England. Only the true prince could tell them that.

Thankfully Prince Edward knew where it was, as he had hidden it himself in a suit of armor. But when they looked, it wasn't there!

Desperate to prove who he was, Edward began to describe the seal in great detail. All at once, Tom laughed and declared, "I know where it is! I didn't realize that what I had taken from the suit of armor was the seal. I have been using it to crack open nuts!" Tom produced the seal, and the entire royal court was satisfied with the explanation.

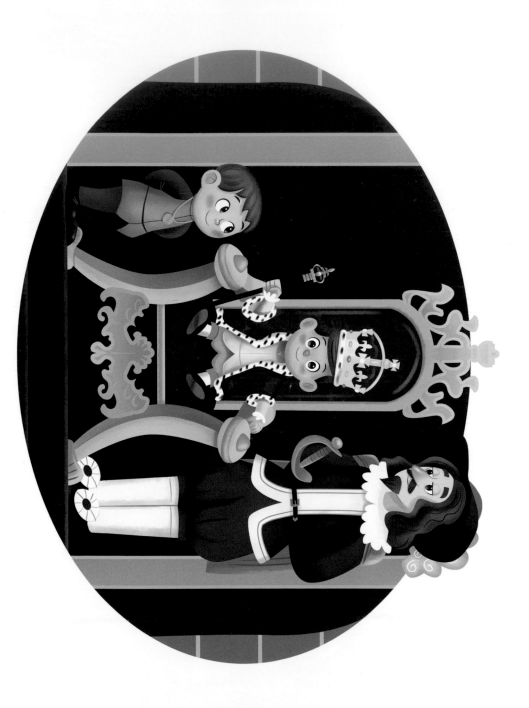

The two boys happily returned to their rightful places. Prince Edward was crowned and became King Edward. He rewarded Tom Canty by a making him a ward of the kingdom, and Miles Hendon was made a knight. Since King Edward had experienced the hardships of poverty, he ruled over his kingdom with kindness and mercy. Long live King Edward!